Black Memorabilia for the Kitchen

Revised and Expanded 2nd Edition

Jan Lindenberger

Schiffer Publishing Ltd®

4880 Lower Valley Road, Atglen, PA 19310 USA

Cast iron mammy spoon rest. "Compliments of Toledo Stove and Range Co." 9". 1930s.

Revised price guide: 1999
Copyright © 1998 by Jan Lindenberger
Library of Congress Catalog Card Number: 98-88134

Designed by Bonnie M. Hensley
Type set in Dutch 801

ISBN: 0-7643-0763-0
Printed in China
1 2 3 4

Published by Schiffer Publishing Ltd.
4880 Lower Valley Road
Atglen, PA 19310
Phone: (610) 593-1777; Fax: (610) 593-2002
E-mail: Schifferbk@aol.com
Please visit our web site catalog at
www.schifferbooks.com

or write for a free catalog.
This book may be purchased from the publisher.
Please include $3.95 for shipping.

In Europe, Schiffer books are distributed by
Bushwood Books
6 Marksbury Rd. Kew Gardens
Surrey TW9 4JF England
Phone: 44 (0)181 392-8585;
Fax: 44 (0)181 392-9876
E-mail: Bushwd@aol.com

Please try your bookstore first.
We are interested in hearing from authors
with book ideas on related subjects.

Acknowledgments

I wish to thank the following people for their help and for sharing their wonderful collections with me, especially Donna Brunello and Roger Lewis for their hospitality and sharing the knowledge of their vast collections. Thanks also to the folks that I may have missed.

Marci Carvalho, Berkley, California
Truly Treasures, Dublin, California
Dixie's Southern Comfort Co-Op, Elk Grove, California
Rykken & Scull, Mill Valley, California
Ed Sherman, Sacramento, California
Sacramento's Antique Center, Sacramento, California
M.L. Bair, Woodland, California
Lavon's Antiques, Simla, Colorado
Black By Popular Demand, Jan Lindenberger, Colorado Springs, Colorado

Cotton toaster cover with stuffed mammy's head. 1940-1950s. $35-45

Lewis/Blalock Collection, Washington, D.C.
Webbs Antique Mall, Centerville, Indiana
Woody Auction, Douglas, Kansas
Roger Lewis, Silver Springs, Maryland
Rose Fontanello, Brooklyn, New York
Ye Olde Canal Antiques, Milan, Ohio
North/South Antiques, Dublin, Ohio
Donna Brunello, Lafayette, Oregon
R. Malsom, Portland, Oregon
Hotel Lincoln Antiques, Manns Choice, Pennsylvania

Pudgy mammy, ceramic string holder.
"Japan." 7". 1935-1940s. $275-300

Preface

As early as the 1700s black items, such as black dolls and fine porcelain figurines, were being produced. Many of them came from Japan, Germany, France, England, Austria, and the United States. From the late 1800s, souvenirs were the biggest market and included such items as figurines, salt and pepper sets, and bisque boys sitting on cotton bales. The black image was also adapted for several useful items for the home. These included note pad holders, tea towels, string holders, and cookie jars, to name a few. Most of the items displayed a rotund mammy or chef working in the kitchen, a butler with a serving tray, or children with watermelons or chickens.

In the late 1950s and early 1960s these stereotypes began to disappear, and the items were no longer being mass produced. The few items that stayed in production through the 1970s did not use the grotesque, exaggerated stereotypes.

In today's secondary market, the stereotyped figures, it seems, are sought by the black collectors. When I ask them why, the answer I receive is that they buy them to show their children how other races have viewed them, and how times and things have changed.

Aunt Jemima Breakfast Club, tin button. 2". 1950s. $10-15

WHERE TO FIND BLACK MEMORABILIA

Shows strictly for black memorabilia.

Unica Shows Unlimited, 5406 9th St. N.W. Washington, D.C. 20011

Sugar Babes, 20 Thorn St. Boston, Ma. 02126

Reproductions: Several of the black collectibles, especially the sought after cookie jars and salt and pepper sets, are being made from the old molds. Sometimes it is very difficult to tell the difference between the old and the new. Especially when they too, bear the maker's mark. When this is done the new item will be just a tad smaller. Usually they are not marked as reproductions. Some of them are being sold as old and when you pay $200 and up for a cookie jar you expect it to be old. If you just want a cookie jar, that's o.k., but to be sold a new one that is misrepresented for an old one is heartbreaking. The old rule still stands. Know your merchandise and know your dealer.

Rare ceramic salt and pepper, mammy and butler. "Japan." 6". $150-175

Contents

Luter's Pure Lard advertising tins, with mammy on the front holding a spoon. Smithfield, Virginia. 4 lb. tin: $150-175, 8 lb. tin: $175-200, 25 lb. tin: $250-275

Cauliflower mammy cookie jar. "McCoy," 1930-1950s. $1200-1500

Introduction

I call my collection "Black memorabilia," though some other terms being used today are Negrobilia, Afro-Americana, mammies, and brown or black face collectibles.

These rapidly growing collectibles are my first love.

My first black purchase was in 1978. A five-piece ceramic band set from "Occupied Japan" came up for sale at auction and I fell totally in love with it. Needless to say it went home with me. The selling price was $24, and I was thought to be totally crazy to be bidding that much. Those days are basically gone; not the craziness, but the low prices. That band set is now selling for $80 per piece.

Years ago, while hunting for those special pieces of black memorabilia, one had to ask the dealer if they had any available. Some non-black dealers were apprehensive to display it, for fear of sparking anger, so they were kept in the back room or under the counter. Years ago, when I had an antique shop, a black woman purchased a black figurine and broke it in front of me. She was very upset that these items were for sale. That is not happening so much anymore. Today, more black people collect these items than any other nationality. The overall feeling has changed, and only rarely do I meet black people who are appalled by these collectibles.

Both the number of collectors and the prices have grown in the past years. It is estimated that the list of collectors has grown to well over 10,000, and each of them has their own list of wants. This market has practically outgrown itself. The average dealer in black memorabilia already has a clientele too numerous to keep up with. As a dealer at the Black memorabilia shows, I have noticed the number of dealers of old, authentic Black memorabilia decreasing. Items are simply unavailable, and avid collectors are not yet seeking to sell any part their collections.

With this reality and with the higher prices, it is hard for the new collector to purchase more than one item at a time. This is not to say there aren't any bargains left out there; there are. And items do come on the market when some collectors sell to weed out their doubles and do an upgrading of their collections. It just takes a vigorous attempt and avid hunting to find them. But isn't that the real joy of it all?

When the old memorabilia can't be found you can always buy the new. There are some wonderful new things being marketed today. Most of the new black collectibles are positive images and well done. The limited edition items are certainly a good investment. But the reproductions are a different story. (See note on page 6 regarding reproductions).

Chef, recipe box. "Fosta Products, U.S.A." Plastic, 3¾x5¼. 1950s. $200-250

Several books about black memorabilia have already been written but, still, all areas have not been covered. This field of collecting covers just about everything. From fine bronzes to dime store souvenirs. I am amazed by the varied collections I have seen, and the unusual things that keep appearing.

In this book I have tried to show a varied selection of black memorabilia from the kitchen, along with the prices at which they are selling today, the size, and approximate date they were manufactured. I truly hope you find this book helpful in your hunting.

Prices differ from coast to coast and auction prices differ from shop prices. Prices are also affected by condition and availability.

Cookie Jars

Cookie jar. Unknown mammy. Ceramic, 10" tall. $750-850

Chef cookie jar. "McCoy" pottery,
10½". 1940-1950s. $500-700

Cookie jar of a unknown mammy
wearing bandanna and holding a
spoon. Ceramic, 1940s-1950s. Cold
painted. 10". $800-950

Soft plastic Aunt Jemima mammy
cookie jar. 10½". 1950s. $350-450

Mammy cookie jars by Mosaic Tile Co. 12½. 1940s. $800-1000

Laughing mammy cookie jar with lid in her belly. "Rockingham Pottery." 8½". 1960s. $350-425

Chef from "Pearl China Pottery." 10". 1940s. $750-850

Complete Pearl China set: Cookie, 10", and Mammy, 11" cookie jars. Large Salty and Peppy, 7½". Small set, 4¼". This set has been personalized in 24 kt. gold. Ceramic, 1940s. $2000-2300

Ceramic mammy cookie jar. Japan. 1940s. $450-500

Top left: Ceramic watermelon
eating mammy, cookie jar. Made
by Gail Gerds from West Allis,
Michigan. Limited edition. Only
100 made. 1990s. $200-300

Top right: Ceramic blinking eye
mammy, cookie jar. Made by
Shirley Corl from Caro, Michigan. Limited edition. Only 100
made. 1990s. $200-300

Bottom right: Ceramic mammy
cookie jar. 1990s. Clay Art.
Made in China. $75-125

Mammy cookie jar. "National Silver Co." pottery. 9". 1940s. $300-350

Mammy cookie jar. "McCoy" pottery. 10½". 1950s. $500-600

Mammy from "Pearl China Pottery." 11". 1940s. $950-1100

Mammy holding flowers cookie jar. "Abingdon Pottery Co." 9¼". 1935-1945. $700-800

Rare mammy head ceramic cracker or biscuit jar, with wicker handle. "Japan." 6". 1930-1940s. $900-1100

Butler ceramic cookie jar. "Japan." 9". 1930-1940s. $750-875

Clown cracker jar with wicker handle. Repainted. 10". 1950s. $250-350

Ceramic little girl "Spice," cookie jar. "J.C.Penny." 14". 1980s. $125-200

Rare cracker jar of mammy with hands folded in front. Ceramic with a wicker handle, marked "Japan." 10". 1930-1940s. $900-1100

Mammy cookie jar. "White Dove Pottery." 9½". 1980s. $125-200

Ceramic chef cookie jar. "Japan." 12½". 1980s. $45-55

Mammy cookie jar. "White Dove Potteries." 9½". 1980s. $250-350

Rockin´ Chair Mammy cookie jar by Carol Gifford. Ceramic. 10". Limited edition. Late 1980s-early 1990s. $250-350

Ceramic cookie jars by Carol Gifford. Watermelon Sammy and Watermelon Mammy. 10".
Limited edition. Late 1980s-early 1990s. $275-400

Ceramic cookie jars by Carol Gifford, Pancake Mammy and The Butler. Limited edition.
Late 1980s-early 1990s. 10". $275-400

"Memories of Mama," ceramic mammy cookie jar. 10½". 1980s. $200-300

"Memories of Mama," ceramic mammy cookie jar. 10½". 1980s. $200-275

"Mandy" cookie jar. "Copyright Omnibus Japan." Ceramic, 9½". 1980s. $275-375

21

Ceramic New Orleans Mammy cookie jar. "Japan." 9½". $60-80

Little girl cookie jar, "Topsy," from Metlox, California. "U.S.A." 1980s. $250-375

Mammy ceramic cookie jar. "Metlox, Calif." 13½". 1980s. $300-400

"Mammy with Bowl" cookie jar. "Metlox, Calif." 13". 1980s. $300-400

Cups and Glasses

Chef cup with hand holding a rolling pin up to the head to form a handle. Pottery. $125-150

Cup and saucer set with banjo playing man on the cup and dancing lady on the saucer. China. 1940s. $60-75

Louis Armstrong ceramic cup. 1980s. $175-200

Pottery cup with nude native dancing woman on the front. 4½" x 3½". 1950s. $100-150

China cup with children playing around tree. 2" x 2½". 1950s. $60-100

Drinking glass with musicians. 12 oz. $15-20

Ceramic drinking glasses, with an embossed nude lady on the front. 7". 1950s. $30-40

Drinking glass with a mammy on front, from the Old Southern Tea Room, Vicksburg, Mississippi. 5". 1945-1950s. $30-35

Frosted drinking glass with handle, and the song of Ole Dan Tucker. 9". $60-75

Set of 6, 12 oz. drinking glasses with dice players painted on them. 1950s. $100-150

Glass bell from "Peg Leg Bates" Country Club, New York. 8" x 2½". $30-40

Decanters

Whiskey decanter with embossed man
holding bottle on front. "Hand painted
Japan." 4". 1940-1950s. $65-80

Banjo man ceramic hand-painted decanter.
11". $300-400

Ceramic decanter of a man sitting on a jug,
and 6 cups. 7½". 1930-1940s. $100-125

Alligator ceramic decanter with cork-lined boy's head in its mouth. Shot glasses hang on its side. Shot glasses are embossed with alligators. 9". "Elvin Japan." 1940s. $175-225

Ceramic decanter of butler holding shot glasses in his pockets and arms. The head comes off to pour. 10". 1930s. $300-400

Ceramic decanter of butler holding tray of shot glasses. The head comes off to pour. 9". 1930s. $300-400

28

Linens

Pot holders of mammy and pappy. Cotton, 1940s. $40-50

Wall-hanging of Haitian people. Appliqué on cotton. Early 1900s. $175-250

Folk art pillow of little girl's head with needle work features and yarn hair with bows. Silk fabric. 12". $125-150

Cotton mammy pot holder. 1940s. $25-35

Cotton little girl in bonnet pot holder. 1950s. $20-25

Cotton handmade pot holders. 1940s. $35-45 set.

Tea caddie or toaster cover featuring mammy holding a stack of pancakes. Cardboard mammy, cotton dress. 12"x 1940s. $90-120

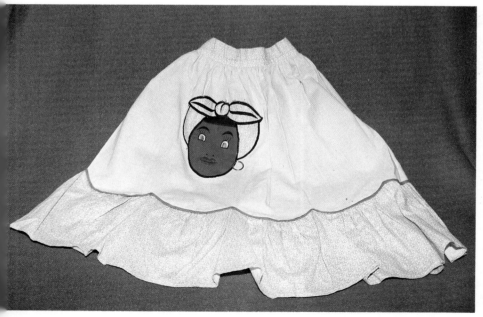

Cotton apron with appliqué mammy's face on pocket. 18" x 21". 1950s. $50-60

Cotton pot holder with embroidery angle. 5". 1950s. $25-35

Clothes pin holder. Wood fiber mammy's head with cloth bag. 17". 1950s. $50-65

Cotton mammy apron with appliqué face. 18" x 19". 1940-1950s. $60-75

Cotton tea towel with a chef flipping pancakes. 1940-1950s. $45-50

Cotton tea towel with butler and mammy. 1940-1950s. $45-50

Cloth 50 lb. flour bag with boy eating cake, "Mammy's Pride," "Larabee Flour Mills Co." 1940s. $125-150

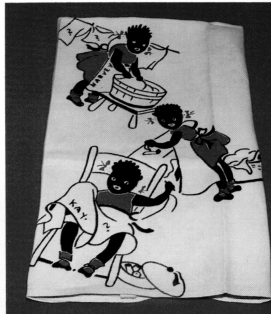

Cotton tea towel with a print of a little girl doing chores. 1940-1950s. $50-60

Tea towel with mammy holding plate of pancakes. 1950s. $50-60

Cotton tea towel featuring a guitar player with a little girl dancing. 1940-1950s. $45-50

Cotton dish towel with mammy washing windows. 1940-1950s. $45-50

Cotton dish towel with mammy washing clothes. 1940-1950s. $45-50

Cotton dish towel printed with a "Cream of Wheat" advertisement. 1950-1960s. $30-35

Set of days-of-the-week cotton dish towels. 1950s. $70-80, set.

Table cloth with a man eating melon with a little girl near a fence. 1950s. $150-175

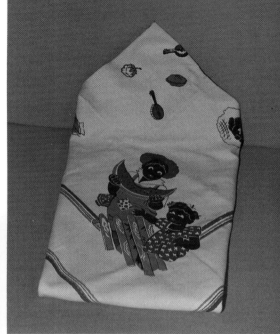

Linen tea towel with an embroidered boy eating melon, and his dog nearby. 1940s. $60-70

Cotton tea towel with mammy carrying a plate of donuts and children watching. 1940-1950s. $55-60

Tea towels with a man playing banjo and a man eating melon. 1950s. $50-55 ea.

Tea towels, cotton with print on material. 1940-1950s. $50-55 ea.

Cotton tea towels with embroidered figures. 1940-1950s. $55-60 ea.

Tea towels. Cotton with print on material. 1940-1950s. $50-55 ea.

Salt and Pepper Sets

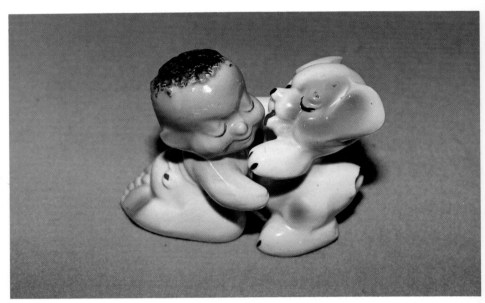

Ceramic little boy with dog. "Vantelligen." 4". $60-75

Ceramic salt and pepper heads. 2½". $75-100

Mammy with baskets on sides as a salt and pepper set. Ceramic, 4½". $100-125

Chef with baskets on side as a salt and pepper set. Ceramic, 4½". $100-125

Chef with coffee pots as a salt and pepper set. Ceramic, marked "Japan." $100-125

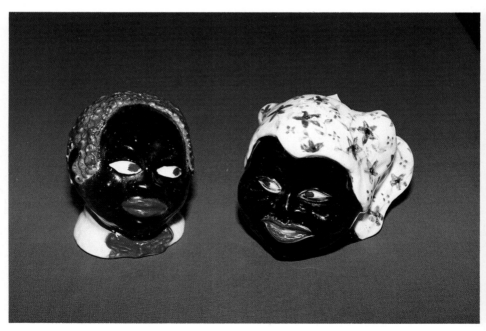

Mammy and butler heads, salt and pepper set. Ceramic, 1940-1950s. $125-150

Girl with melon butter knife and salt and pepper. Ceramic, marked "Japan." 5". $75-100

Bobbing head native with melon salt and pepper set. China, 3". 1940-1950s. $75-100

Ceramic salt and pepper set, boy with melon. 5". 1940-1950. $75-100

Boy holding melon, ceramic salt and pepper set. 5". 1940s. $75-100

Little girl eating melon, ceramic salt and pepper set. 5". 1940-1950s. $75-100

Native eating melon, ceramic salt and pepper. 3¼". $75-100

Bobbing head native women with melon slices, bisque salt and pepper sets. Germany. Heads are salts and the melon slices are peppers. 3½". $75-125

Ceramic busts
of boys as salts
and melons as
peppers. 2½".
1940s. $65-80

Boy's head and melon, ceramic salt and
pepper. Japan. 3". $75-100

Man's head with melon slice, ceramic salt
and pepper set. 2½". 1935-1940s. $65-90

Native with melon, ceramic salt and pepper set. Man, 5"; melon, 3½". 1940-1950s. $60-75

Natives on corn, ceramic salt and pepper set. "Japan." 3½". $70-80

Natives on egg plant, ceramic salt and pepper set. "Japan." 5½" x 2". $70-80

Natives on cabbages, ceramic salt and pepper set "Japan." 3". $70-80

Natives on carrot, ceramic salt and pepper. "Japan." 3½". $70-80

Elephant carrying native boy, with the baskets on side as a salt and pepper set. Ceramic, 4½". $70-80

Native man and tree, ceramic salt and pepper set. 4½". $60-75

Kissing natives, ceramic salt and pepper set. Japan. 3". $60-75

Native mama with baby on her lap, pottery salt and pepper set. 4". $70-85

Boy and elephant, ceramic salt and pepper set. 7". $75-90

Blackamoors with tree, ceramic salt and pepper set. Japan, 3". $60-75

Native on alligator's back, salt and pepper
set. 3½". 1940-1950s. $65-75

Native sitting on alligator's back, ceramic
salt and pepper set. 3½". 1940-1950s.
$75-85

Jonah and the whale, ceramic salt and
pepper set. "Japan." 3½". $75-100

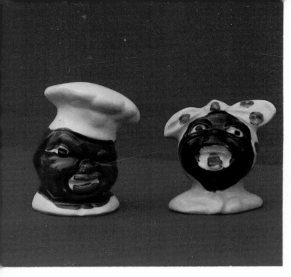

Busts of mammy and chef, ceramic salt and pepper. "Japan." 2-7/8". $75-100

Mammy and chef, pottery salt and pepper set. 3". 1945-1950s. $60-75

Native men, ceramic salt and pepper. 4". 1945-1950s. $50-60

Busts of chef and mammy, pottery salt and pepper set. 3". 1940s. $65-75

Pottery figurines of natives. 4¼". 1940-1950s. $50-65

Native boy and girl on drums, wooden salt and pepper set. 2½". $60-75

Chef and mammy heads, salt and pepper set (repainted). 4". $45-55.

Boys in turtleneck sweaters, ceramic oil and pepper containers (salt and vinegar missing). "Japan." Pepper: 4¾"; Oil: 6". 1930-1940s. $90-110, set ($75 ea. mint condition).

Chef and mammy, plastic salt and pepper set in the box. "Japan." 2½" x 3". 1950-1960s. $55-70

Salt shakers of Luzianne cooks advertising "Luzianne Coffee." $75-100 ea.

Salt and pepper set of a boy and girl on a tray. "Japan." 3". 1940s. $75-100

Salt and pepper set with a girl and boy in basket. "Japan." 4". 1940-1950s. $75-100

Pottery salt and pepper clowns. "Japan." 3". 1950s. $45-55

Ceramic salt and pepper young chefs. "Japan." 3" x 1". $50-75

Wooden elephant for tooth picks, with natives salt and pepper set. 1950s. $40-50

Girl and boy ceramic valentine salt and pepper set. 5". 1940s. $75-100

Boy with a heart for a little girl, ceramic salt and pepper set. 5". 1940-1950s. $90-125

Chef and mammy, ceramic salt and pepper set. Souvenirs of Crystal Beach, Florida. "Japan." $55-65

Chef with water buckets, ceramic salt and pepper set. "Japan." 5". $60-75

Calypso plaster salt and pepper. 4½". $50-65

Native boy and girl with blinking eyes, sitting on log, plaster salt and pepper set. 4". $65-75

Wooden salt and pepper set. Salt and pepper comes out of the side of the holder. "Japan." 1950s. $65-75

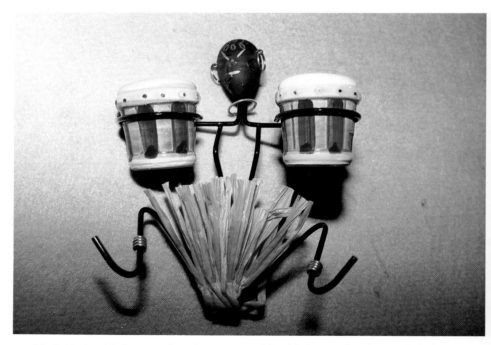

Native lady with drums, salt and pepper set. Metal lady, wooden drums. 5½". $50-60

Mammy and pappy, holding his hat, chalk salt and pepper set. 3". 1945-1950s. $50-60

Rastus and Lisa, wooden salt and pepper set. 3". 1950s. $45-55

Large head boys, ceramic salt and pepper set. "Japan." 3½". 1945-1950s. $65-75

Native boys sitting, ceramic salt and pepper set. "Japan." 3". 1945-1950s. $45-55

Ceramic salt and pepper, chefs holding fruit. 3½". $55-65

Native heads, salt and pepper set. Wooden head, celluloid caps. 2½". $45-55

Crying chef holding a dead chicken, smiling chef holding the guilty cat, ceramic salt and pepper set. 1940-1950s. $100-125

Porter carrying luggage, ceramic salt and pepper set. "Japan." 5". 1940s. $75-100

Porter and luggage, ceramic salt and pepper set. Porter, 2¾"; luggage, 1". 1940s. $75-100

Grandma in rocking chair, ceramic salt and pepper set. 3½". $75-100

Native man (salt) and drum (pepper) ceramic set. 3½". 1945-1950. $60-75

Figurine of porter holding leather bags. Pot metal, 1930-1940s. $125-150

Ceramic mammy salt and pepper set. "Japan." 1930-1940s. 5".

Chef and mammy, ceramic salt and pepper set (repainted). National Silver. 4½". $65-90

Rare ceramic salt and pepper, mammy and chef. "Japan." 5". $150-175

Ceramic salt and pepper, butler and
mammy. 5". $150-175

Mammy and butler, ceramic salt and
pepper set. "Japan." 6". 1940-1950s.
$100-125

Mammy and butler, ceramic salt and
pepper set. "Japan." 6". 1930-1940.
$150-175

Salt and pepper, mammy and chef.
"Japan." 5" 1940-1950s. $60-75

Chef and cook, ceramic salt and pepper set. Richmond, Virginia souvenirs. 4". $60-75

Mammy and chef, ceramic salt and pepper set. "Japan." 3". 1940-1950s. $45-55

Mammy and chef, ceramic salt and pepper set. "Japan." 2". 1940-1950s. $55-70

Salt and pepper set of chicks coming out of eggs. The black chick has large lips. "Japan." 2". $40-50

Mammy and chef, ceramic salt and pepper set. "Japan." 8". 1940-1950s. $100-125

Mammy and chef, ceramic salt and pepper set. "Japan." 5" 1950s. $65-90

Mammy and chef, ceramic vinegar and oil. "Japan." 5¼". 1940-1950s. $125-150

Ceramic salt and pepper, chef and mammy holding spoons, 8½". "Japan." 1940s. $125-150

Salt and pepper, chef and cook. Ceramic with green/gold trim, 5". 1940s. $65-75

Hard to find salt and pepper, ceramic chef and mammy. 1½" x 4½". $90-125.

Chef and cook, ceramic salt and pepper set (repainted). "Japan." $65-75

Mammy and chef, salt and pepper set with 22 kt. gold. "Pearl China Co." 4½". 1940s. Personalized. $125-150

Mammy and chef, salt and pepper set with 22 kt gold. "Pearl China Co." 7½". 1940s. Personalized. $175-200

Mammy and chef, ceramic salt and pepper set. "Hand painted." 5½". 1940-1950s. $75-100

Mammy and chef, salt and pepper set. Ceramic with blue/gold trim. 5". 1940s. $65-75

Mammy and chef, salt and pepper set. Ceramic with green/gold trim. 5". 1940s. $65-75

Ceramic salt and pepper, chef and cook. 4½" x 2½". 1945-1950. $60-75

Ceramic salt and pepper set. Clay Art. Made in China. $30-40

Chef and cook, ceramic salt and pepper set. "Japan." 4½". $45-50

Chef and mammy, ceramic salt and pepper set. "Japan." 5". 1940-1950s. $60-75

Ceramic salt and pepper, chef and maid. "Leftons, Japan." 6". 1945-1950s. $75-100

Mammy and chef, ceramic salt and pepper set. 4". 1950s. $55-65

Mammy and chef, ceramic salt and pepper set. "Japan." 3". 1940-1950s. $50-60

Salt and pepper, ceramic mammy and chef. 3".$55-65

Chef and mammy, salt and pepper set. "I'm Salty" and "I'm Peppy" written on hats. Gold trim on white ceramic. 3". 1950s. $50-60

Mammies, chalk salt and pepper set. "Japan." 3". 1940s. $50-60

Fat mammy and chef, chalkware souvenir salt and pepper set. 2-7/8". 1940s. $40-50

Mammy and chef with hands on sides, ceramic salt and pepper set. 3". $40-45

Chef and mammy, ceramic salt and pepper set. "Japan." 4½". $75-100

Young mammy and chef, ceramic salt and pepper set. 3". 1950s. $60-75

Mammy and chef, salt and pepper set. Ceramic, yellow/gold trim. 5". 1940s. $50-60

Mammy and chef, ceramic salt and pepper set. "Japan." 4". 1940s. $60-70

Old man and woman, ceramic salt and pepper set. "Japan." 1935-1940s. $50-65

Blackamoors with baskets on heads. Ceramic. 4" $35-40

Salt and pepper, ceramic Blackamoors. 4" $25-30

Ceramic figurines, boys with banjos. "Japan." 2". 1950s. $40-50

Wooden salt and pepper, native boy and girl. 5½" x 2". $40-50

Wooden salt and pepper, native man and lady. $45-55

Ceramic pepper shaker of a woman holding a bouquet of flowers. 6". 1955-1960. $35-40

Chef, ceramic salt shaker. "Japan." 1950-1960s. $20-25

Mammy, rare ceramic salt shaker. "Japan." 3". 1930-1940s. $30-40

New ceramic salt and pepper set of mammy and chef. "Metlox." 6½". $60-75

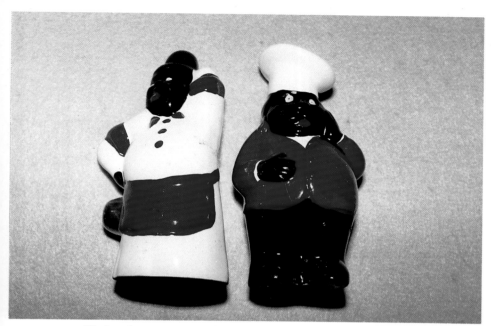

Chef and mammy, ceramic salt and pepper set. 1990s. 6". $60-75

Little boy and girl, ceramic salt and pepper set. 2½". 1980s. $40-50

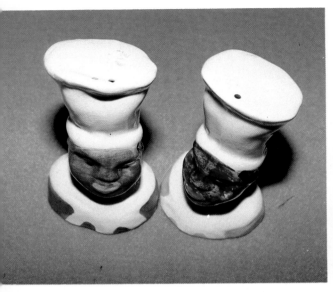

Chef heads, ceramic salt and pepper set. 3". 1990s. $40-50

Banjo boys, ceramic salt and pepper set. 2½". 1990s.$40-50

Chef and mammy, ceramic salt and pepper set. 6½". 1990s. $40-50

Chef and cook, ceramic salt and pepper set. "Metlox from Calif." Newer but not made anymore. 7½". $60-75

Ceramic salt and pepper set with tooth pick holder, with "New Orleans" scene on front. 5". 1990s. $45-50

Mammy with eggs in basket, ceramic salt and pepper set, 1990. 4". $50-60

Singer and horn player, ceramic salt and pepper set, 1990. Ceramic. 3½". $50-60

Rio Rita, new ceramic salt and pepper set. 3½". $50-60

Man's and woman's heads, ceramic salt and pepper set. Wisecarver. 4". 1980s. $55-65

Ceramic salt and pepper. The hands are the salt and the head is the pepper. 3½". $70-90

Plastic Golliwog band players, salt and pepper set. 3½". $55-75

Spoon Rests and Platters

Chef, ceramic spoon rest and wall hanger. 9". 1940-1950s. $85-110

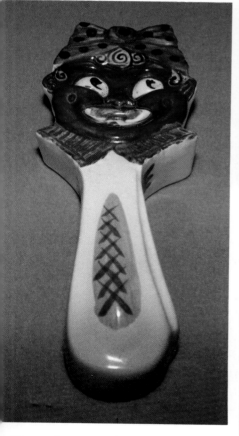

Mammy bust, ceramic spoon rest. "Japan." 9". $175-200

Mammy sitting on frying pan, ceramic spoon rest. 5½". $80-100

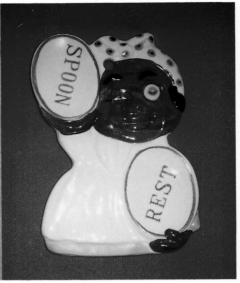

Mammy spoon rest. "Rockingham Pottery Japan." 8". 1940-1950s. $125-165

Ceramic spoon rest. Mammy with blinking eye. "Japan." 8". 1950s. $125-150

Native face, ceramic spoon rest. "Italy 231." 6" x 6½". $75-100

Ceramic mammy platter. 1990s. Clay Art. Made in China. $50-65

String Holders
and Wall Pockets

Mammy, ceramic string holder. 7",
1935-1940s. $275-325

Terra cotta mammy
string holder.
1940s. $275-350

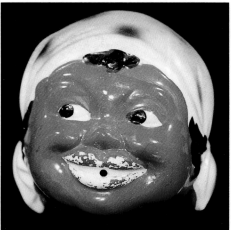

Ceramic Mammy
string holder. Japan.
$300-400

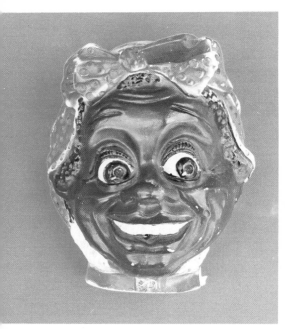

Mammy, plastic string holder. 8". 1930-1945. $250-350

Mammy, rare plaster string holder. 7½". "Japan." 1930-1945. $275-375

Rare pottery wall pocket of mammy's head. 1945-1950s. $250-300

Ceramic wall pocket, chef with cooking utensils. 9". 1950s. $200-300

Mammy, wall string holder. Plaster, 5½". 1940s. $250-300

Mammy, wall string holder. Plaster, 8". 1940s. $275-375

Chef holding spoon and salt, chalk string holder. "Map Co." 7½". 1949. $175-225

Butler, plaster string holder. "Fredricksburg Art pottery." 7". 1930-1940s. $275-375

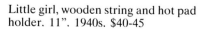

Little girl, wooden string and hot pad holder. 11". 1940s. $40-45

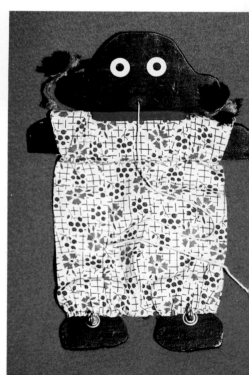

Folk art string holder. Wooden little girl with cotton dress and yarn hair. 8". 1930s. $65-75

Wall pocket of boy and girl with big smiles. Ceramic, 5¾". 1940-1950s. $175-200 ea.

Ceramic mammy wall pocket. 1950s. $175-200

Mammy, cardboard paper towel holder. 13" x 12". 1940s. $175-225

Copper mammy with oil cloth clothes, wall plaque pot holder hanger. 11½". 1940-1950s. $225-275

Ceramic wall pocket/planter. 1940s/50s. $100-125

Mammy sitting on stove, ceramic wall hanger, planter. 5" 1940-1950s. $100-125

Mammy, note holder. Plastic, 6" 1930-1940s. $100-125

Wooden folk art holder for pot holders, mammy and butler. $100-125

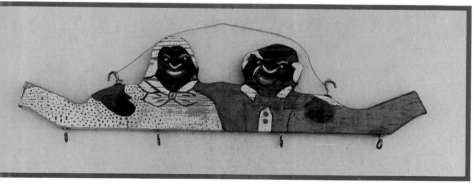

Folk art, wooden wall-hanging holder for pot holders. 12". 1940s. $75-85

Wooden folk art
mammy wall hanger
for pot holders. 12".
1950s. $35-40

Ceramic mammy with
bouquet of flowers.
Japan. 1940s/50s.
$300-375

Bisque mammy potpourri
holder. (It has 3 separate
pieces). 1980s. $25-35

Hot Pad & Note Holders and Plaques

Wooden wall plaques with mammy faces attached, used as holders for pot holders. "Japan." 5". 1940s. $50-60 ea.

Wooden wall plaque of little girl with a bow in her hair. "Hang dat heh an you'll sho find it." 9" 1940s. $60-75

Plastic wall hanger for pot holders. 1950s. $45-55

Mammy, wooden folk art note holder. 9". 1930s. $50-65

Wooden folk art hot pad holder. 9". 1920-1930s. $50-65

Mammy, wooden note holder. 8". 1930-1940s. $50-65

Souvenir wooden mammy, hot pad holder. "Burbank, Ca" 6½". 1950s. $50-75

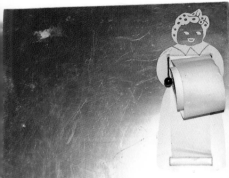

Copper magnetic note holder with mammy painted on front. 11" x 14". 1940-1950s. $100-125

Bottom left: Wooden mammy, hot pad holder. 7". 1940-1950s. $65-75

Bottom right: Wooden mammy, hot pad holder. 7½". 1950s. $50-60

Wooden mammy hot pad holder. 1950s. $60-75

Wooden note holder. The roof is raised to leave a note. 7". 1945-1950. $75-100

Mammy, wall-hanging board with "Chore Girl" scrubber. 1940s. $75-125

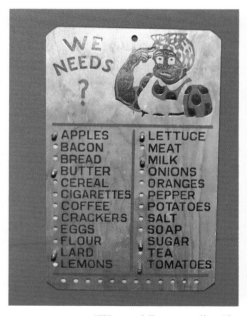

"We needs" grocery list. "Japan." 8¼" x 6". 1940s. $65-95

"I hasta have" grocery list. 11½" x 5½". 1940s. $65-95

Mammy, plastic note pad holder. 10¼".
1940-1950s. $75-100

Wall-hanging mammy, chalkware memo
pad holder. 9". 1940s. $65-90

Chef, plastic grocery list holder. "ABM
23." 10½". 1950s. $75-100

Plaster note pad holder of chef holding paper, with the pencil as a broom. 9¾". 1940s. $75-100

Wall plaque. The chef is made of plaster. 1940s. $80-100

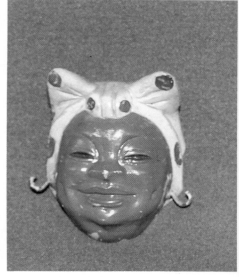

Wall-hanging plaster mammy. 4". 1940s. $50-65

Mammy, chalk hanger for pot holders. 5½". 1940-1950s. 50-65

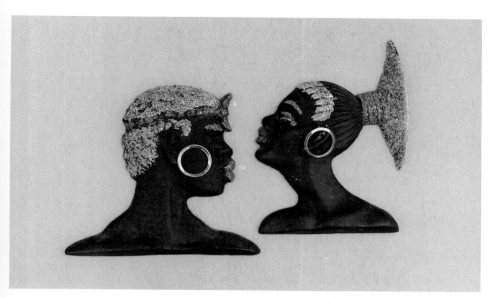

Pair of natives, wall-hanging pot metal plaques. 7". 1950s. $75-125 pair

Chef and mammy, chalk plaques for hanging pot holders. 6". 1940s. $60-80 pair

Wooden mammy note holder. 10". 1940s. $60-75

String holders of a man and a woman. Terra cotta, 6". 1940-1950s. $80-100 ea.

Three wall-hanging busts of Indian blacks. Terra cotta, 2½". 1930s. $85-110, set

Little Black Sambo, chalkware wall plaque. 7¾". 1940-1950s. $75-100

African woman, wall plaque of highly
polished mahogany wood, with intricate
work. 13" x 13". 1930s. $575-700

Wooden memo pad. 1950s. $65-80

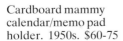

Plastic memo pad holder. 1950s. $55-75

Cardboard mammy
calendar/memo pad
holder. 1950s. $60-75

Tea Pots and Pitchers

Tea pot from a very rare Weller Pottery Co. set. The mammy's head with the big smile is the li
This belongs to a set with a batter bowl, cookie jar, syrup pitcher, creamer and sugar. 1938.
$1000-1300, tea pot only.

Elephant with native on back, China tea pot. "Japan." 7½" x 8". 1930s. $120-150

Elephant with native on back, China tea pot. "Japan." 6"x 6½". 1930s. $120-150

China tea pot with native sitting on top of camel. "Japan." 6" x 10". 1930-1940s. $250-275

China tea pot with native sitting on elephant's back. "Japan." 9½" x 7". 1930-1950s. $225-275

Pitcher advertising Canadian Club liquor. 5½". 1960s. $80-100

Chef, ceramic tea pot. "Japan." 1940-1950s. $125-175

108

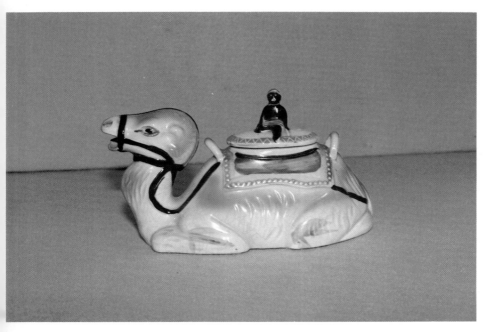

Camel ceramic tea pot, with sitting native boy on the lid. "Japan." 10". 1930-1940s. $185-250

Elephant with native on back, China tea pot. "Japan." 8" x 9½". 1930s. $150-200

Syrup pitcher with Little Black Sambo on front. Satin glass jar with a plastic lid. 11". $225-275

Mammy, ceramic tea pot. "Japan." 6" x 8". 1930-1940s. $400-500

Pottery milk pitcher. "Mexico,"
1945-1955. $500-700

Miscellaneous Kitchen Items

Cook, four-piece ceramic spice set in wooden holder. 3¼". 1950s. $125-165

Chef, four-piece ceramic spice set in a wooden rack. "Japan." 10" x 5". $125-165

Mammy, new salt and pepper with tooth-pick holder. "Japan." $40-50

Mammy, clothes sprinkler. Ceramic, 8". 1940-1950s. $225-250

Mammy, ceramic candle holder. "Japan." 5". 1940-1950s. $100-150

Mammy and chef, ceramic creamers. "Japan." 3½". 1945-1950s. $125-150 ea.

Calypso, ceramic creamer. 1940-1950s. $75-100

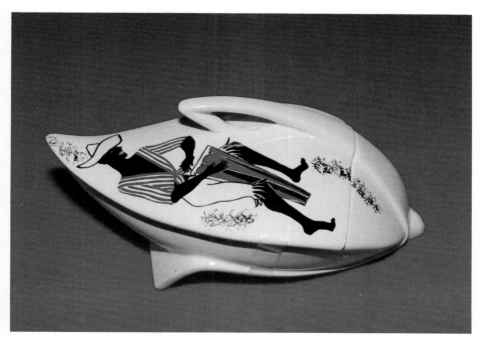

Calypso, ceramic sugar bowl. 1940-1950s. $75-100

Yellow chef, ceramic pie bird. "Japan." 4".
1940-1950s.

Ceramic salad set, with calypso figures
(came with third untensil and rack) 7" x 2".
1950s. $75-100 complete

Farmer, whisk broom. Plastic brush, wooden bust. 8". 1940-1950s. $75-95

Mammy whisk broom. Plastic brush, wooden bust. 7". 1940-1950s. $70-85

Chef and mammy heads, ceramic cream and sugar. "Japan." 3½". 1930s. $175-200 set

Chef, China pie bird, 5". "Germany." 1930-1940s. $200-225

Fireman, sugar bowl. Part of a hard-to-find set, it came with a creamer, salt and pepper, and tea pot. Pottery, 6" x 4". 1940s. $45-60

Chef and mammy jelly jars. "Japan." 4¼". 1930-1940s. $225-250

Mammy, ceramic cheese shaker. 6". 1940s. $60-75

Ceramic condiment set with mammy and barrels. 6½". $175-200

Ceramic figurine of mammy holding basket on her head. 6½". 1950s. $75-100

Mammy carrying basket on her head, ceramic planter. 6½". 1950s. $75-100

Mammy and chef, one-piece vinegar and oil. "Japan." 5½". 1940s. $175-200

Mammy and chef, one-piece oil and vinegar ceramic cruet set. 5½". 1940s. $175-200 mint condition.

Mammy with laundry basket, soap pad holder. "Brayton Laguna." 9". 1940-1950s. $200-225

Little girl with clothes basket for scouring pad. Ceramic, 5". 1940s. $150-175

Mammy, recipe box. "Fosta Products. U.S.A." Plastic, 3¾" x 5¼". 1950s. $250-275 ea.

Native, pottery sugar jar. "Made in England." 9½". 1950s. $150-175

Baking pan for biscuits. The mammy on the front is advertising Calumet baking powder. 1930s. $75-100

Wooden figurine of maid holding scrubber and brush. 6". 1950-1960s. $50-75

Mammy broom cover. Cotton dress. 1980s. $50-60

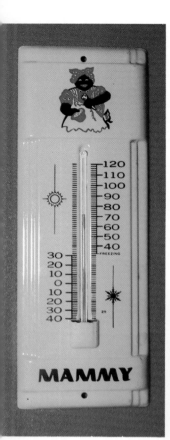

Tin thermometer with mammy on the front. 1980s. $20-30

Rare little girl thermometer. Pressed fiber wood, 5". $200-250

Native boy and girl, China thermometers. "Japan." 1940-1950s. $60-90 ea.

Rare mammy cooking egg timer on a tin hanger for pot holders. 8". 1940-1950s. $225-300

THREE MINUTE EGG TIMER

Chef, ceramic egg timer. "Japan." 4".
1940-1950s. $100-125

Golliwog, bisque egg timer. "England."
1920s. $200-250

Chef as egg timer. "Japan." Ceramic, 3".
1940s. $125-150

Bell with man playing banjo on top.
Ceramic, 4". "Japan." $35-45

Mammy bell. Tin with a wooden head,
1950s. 4". $25-30

Products and Advertising

Luter's enamel advertising sign. $400-500

Gold Dust Twins

The Fairbanks Company of Chicago, Illinois had the idea for the Gold Dust twins from a cartoon in the English humor magazine *Punch*, showing two black children washing each other in a tub. It read "Warranted to wash clean and not to fade." It was drawn for the package in 1887. At one time the twins were among the best known commercial symbols in America.

Gold dust Scouring Cleanser, by Lever Bros. 5". 1915-1920s. $70-90 ea.

Gold Dust Soap Powder. 9" x 6". 1920-1930s. $75-100

Magazine ad for Gold Dust Twins Soap Powder. 11" x 14". 1920s. $40-50

128

Box of "Sahara Dates," product of Algeria. 5" x 4". 1930-1940s. $200-225

Tin for "Old Reliable Peanut Butter," Suffolk, Virginia. 5". 1920-1930s. $250-300

Old Virginia "Herring Roe" oyster tin. Tilghman Packing Co. 1930s. $175-200

"Flavor Glow Gravy Sauce." Jacob Foods, West Chester, Pennsylvania. 4½". 1940s. $40-50

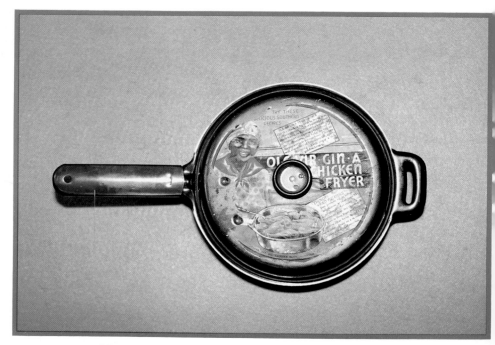

Ole Vir-Gin-A chicken fryer. 10". "U.S.A." 1940s. $75-100

Cardboard sign from restaurant. 1940s/50s. $75-100

Jumbo Salted Nut tin. Kelly Peanut Co., Boston, Mass. 1920s. $450-550

Menu from Sambo's restaurant. (Inside and out) 1950s. $75-100

Cookbooks

Southern Cook of Fine Old Dixie Recipes. $75-100

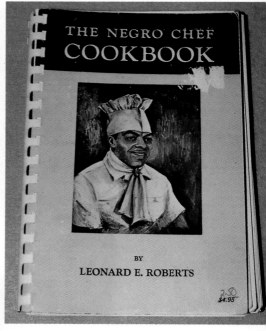

Cook book, *The Negro Chef.* Paperback. $65-90

Aunt Jemima recipe booklet. 1950s. $35-45

Aunt Caroline's Dixieland Recipes. 1930s. $75-100

Fisher's Blendbrand, recipe book. $50-60

Aunt Jemima

In 1889, the vaudeville team of Baker and Farrell sang a song about Aunt Jemima which caught the ear of Chris L. Rutt, a businessman from St. Joseph, Missouri. Rutt had just come up with the idea for a self-raising pancake mix. Thus, Aunt Jemima pancake mix was born. Rutt later sold the business to the R.L. Davis Company.

At the Columbian Exposition in Chicago, in 1893, the Davis Company set up a booth and served over one million pancakes. Nancy Green was hired to portray Aunt Jemima and to make the pancakes. Green came from Montgomery County, Kentucky. Until her death in 1923, she traveled with the company portraying Aunt Jemima.

The grotesque character of a black mammy remained on the package until 1917 when she was re-drawn as a real person. She still remained a stereotyped household worker. In 1924 the Quaker Oats Company bought the recipe and the Aunt Jemima name, and has made and sold the mix since.

Rare Aunt Jemima and Uncle Mose, cream and sugar. "F and F Mold Co., Dayton, Ohio." 1950s. Greenish yellow. 2¼" x 2½". (It also came in light blue, which is also rare.) $350-450

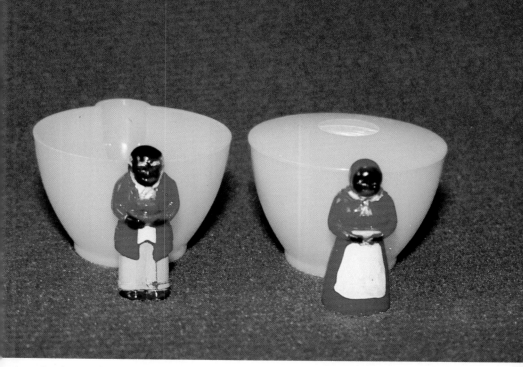

Aunt Jemima and Uncle Mose, cream and sugar. "F & F Tool and Die, Dayton, Ohio." 2¼ x 2½". 1950s. $150-

Edith Wilson was hired by the company in the 1950s. It's her picture that we remember today. Edith Wilson was born in 1897 and recorded a record in 1921. She also had a part on the "Amos and Andy" show. For over 18 years, she portrayed Aunt Jemima. It has been said that forty different woman portrayed Aunt Jemima in the history of the pancake mix.

Some of the items the company used as premiums were a cardboard puzzle, a tin pin, a four-piece set of Aunt Jemima family dolls (which came in plastic and cloth), a lighter, the Luzianne mammy salt and pepper set, a sewing kit, a metal pancake mold, and recipe books and cards.

The first plastic premium put out by the company, in 1949, was the syrup pitcher. This was taped to the box as a giveaway. The other items were mail-in offers with box tops from the pancake mix. There were the salt and pepper sets (which came in two sizes), the creamer and the sugar bowl (which had a lid), a six-piece spice set with the copper coated rack, a plastic spice rack, the hard plastic mammy cookie jar, and the soft plastic mammy cookie jar.

Aunt Jemima plastic cookie jar. "F & F Tool & Die, Dayton Ohio." 12". 1950s. $400-550

Aunt Jemima, plastic syrup pitcher. "F & F Tool and Die, Dayton, Ohio." 5½". 1950s. $65-80

Aunt Jemima and Uncle Mose, plastic salt and pepper set. " F & F Tool and Die, Dayton, Ohio." 5". 1950s. $55-75

Aunt Jemima and Uncle Mose, plastic salt and pepper set. "F & F Tool and Die, Dayton, Ohio." 3½". 1950s. $50-65

Aunt Jemima, tin button. "Adcraft Mfg. Co." 2". 1950s. $15-20

Aunt Jemima, Uncle Mose, Diana, Wade, oil cloth stuffed dolls. 9" & 12". 1950s.
$400-500 set

Boxes of Aunt Jemima pancake mix. 1980s. $20-30 each.

Boxes of Aunt Jemima pancake mix. 1980s. $20-30 each.

Coupon for three pieces of the Aunt Jemima spice set, which could be purchased for 50 cents and one box top from Aunt Jemima ready mix. The same price would get you the copper rack. 17". 1950s. $25-35

Coupon for the Aunt Jemima rag doll. Fifty cents and one box top from Aunt Jemima ready mix would purchase a doll. The same was true for the uncle Mose, Diana, Wade dolls. 17". 1950s. $25-35

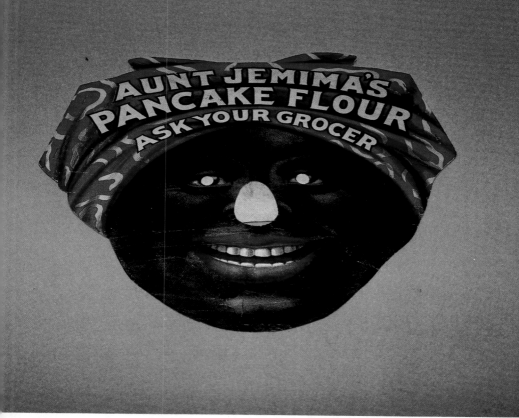

Halloween Mask of Aunt Jemima. Cardboard with advertising on the back. 10½". Early 1900s. $400-500

Aunt Jemima spice rack and spices. "F & F Tool & Die, Dayton, Ohio." 12" rack; $550-650, 4" spices; $60-70 ea. 1950s.

Aunt Jemima paper hats were advertising give-aways. 1950s. $75-100 ea.

Aunt Jemima recipe books. 1950s. 4" x 6". $35-45 ea.

Aunt Jemima cotton bag,
filled with corn meal. "The
Quaker Oats Co." 25 lbs.
$200-300

Aunt Jemima starched cotton
banner. 55" x 34". 1953. $650-750

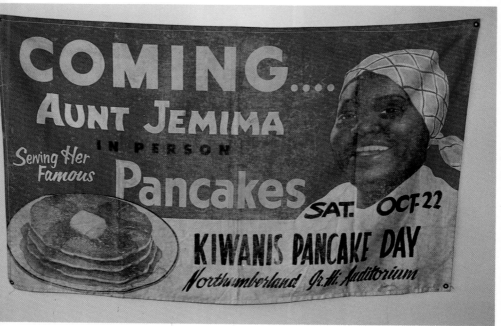

Bibliography

Carson, Jeanette. *Black Ethnic Collectible Magazine*: Hyattsville, Maryland. Volume 4 #5. August, 1991.

Congdon-Martin, Douglas. *Images in Black, 150 Years of Black Collectibles.* Atglen, Pennsylvania: Schiffer Publishing, Ltd. 1990.

Morgan, Hal. *Symbols of America.* New York, New York: Viking penguin Inc. 1986.

Rainwater, Dorothy. *American Spoons Souvenir & Historical,* Pennsylvania: Thomas Nelson & Son & Everybody's Press. 1968

Reno, Dawn E. *Collecting Black American.* New York: Crown Publishers Inc. 1986.

Smith, Darrell A. *Black Americana, A Personal Collection.* Minneapolis, Minnesota: Star Press, Inc. 1988.

Young, Jackie. *Black Collectibles: Mammy and Her Friends.* Atglen, Pennsylvania: Schiffer Publishing, Ltd. 1988.

World Book Encyclopedia. 1991.